All the water in the world

W9-CCU-430

All the water

SCHOLASTIC INC.

in the world

by George Ella Lyon

and Katherine Tillotson

...is all the water

in the world.

Water

flows from the hose.

It wobbles

in blue pools.

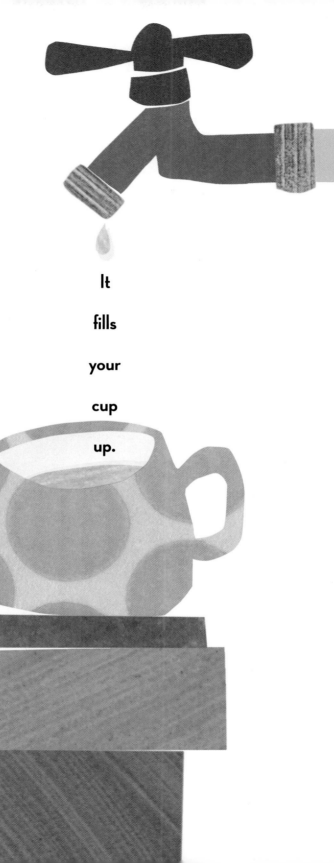

It

fills

your

cup

up.

But where

does it come

from?

Water doesn't come.
It goes.
Around.

That rain

that cascaded from clouds

and meandered down mountains,

that wavered over waterfalls

then slipped into rivers

and opened into oceans,

that rain has been here before.

Thirsty air

   licks it from lakes

      sips it from ponds

         guzzles it from oceans

up
s
w
i
r
l
s

and this wet air

till it's crowded into clouds

where it hangs hotly around

till cool air bumps through

honey, those clouds

and

just

let

it go

and rain

rain

rain!

Tap dance

avalanche

stampede
of drips and drops and drumming—

a wealth of water.

But far away

it's a different day—

no sound but wind

empty cup again

dry grasses rustle

dirt's just dust.

Everything
waits

for an open gate

in a wall of clouds

for rain sweet and loud

to fill the well

and start the stream.

Honey,
living things dream
of water

for all to drink
use in tub or sink
wash in, splash in.

This wet wonder
means grow
means life will flow

through tigers
through trees.

Through you

and through me.

All
all

All together

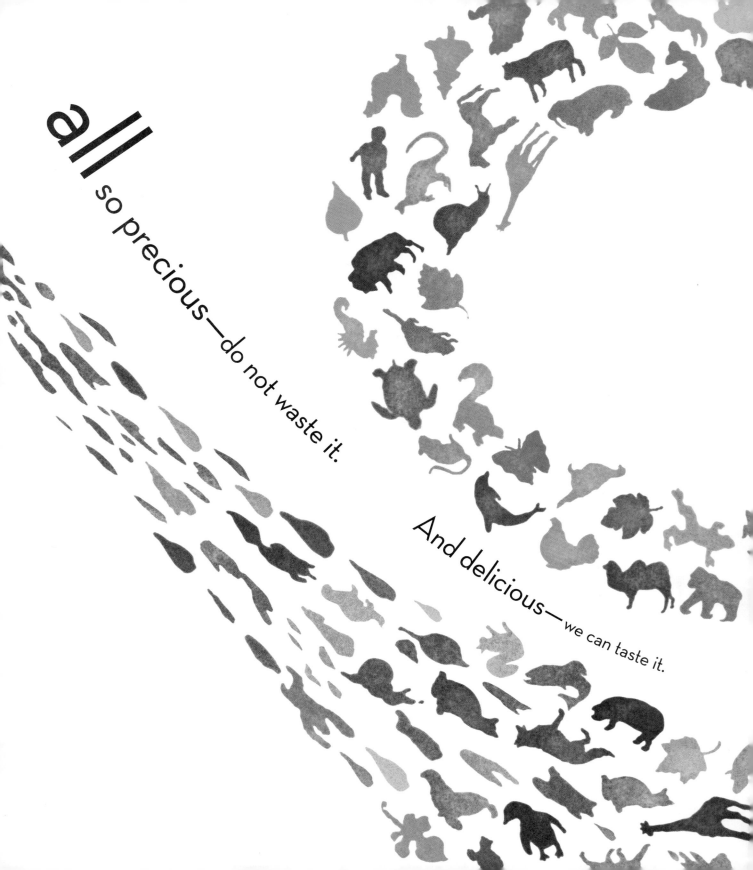

all so precious—do not waste it.

And delicious— we can taste it.

Keep it clear, keep it clean . . .

keep Earth

green!

For Pete Seeger, Wendell Berry, Gurney Norman,
and all who work to save the water of life

And for Bernie Stoddard, who is just learning to swim in it
—G. E. L.

For Dick Jackson, dowser, editor, friend
—K. T.

No part of this publication may be reproduced,
stored in a retrieval system, or transmitted in any form
or by any means, electronic, mechanical, photocopying,
recording, or otherwise, without written permission of
the publisher. For information regarding permission,
write to Atheneum Books for Young Readers, an imprint of
Simon & Schuster Children's Publishing Division,
1230 Avenue of the Americas, New York, NY 10020.

ISBN 978-0-545-55833-4

Text copyright © 2011 by George Ella Lyon.
Illustrations copyright © 2011 by Katherine Tillotson.
All rights reserved. Published by Scholastic Inc.,
557 Broadway, New York, NY 10012, by arrangement with
Atheneum Books for Young Readers, an imprint of Simon & Schuster
Children's Publishing Division. SCHOLASTIC and associated logos are
trademarks and/or registered trademarks of Scholastic Inc.

12 11 10 9 8 7 6 5 4 3 2   13 14 15 16 17 18/0

Printed in the U.S.A.   40

First Scholastic printing, February 2013

Book design by Ann Bobco
The text for this book is set in Neutraface.
The illustrations for this book are rendered digitally.